THE BIG BOOK OF COUNTRY

Exclusive Distributors:
Music Sales Limited
8/9 Frith Street, London W1D 3JB, England.

Order No. HLE90002187
ISBN 1-84449-578-7

Cover design by Paula Snell Design
Printed in the USA

Your Guarantee of Quality
As publishers, we strive to produce
every book to the highest commercial
standards. The book has been carefully
designed to minimise awkward page
turns and to make playing from it a real
pleasure. Throughout, the printing and
binding have been planned to ensure
a sturdy, attractive publication which
should give years of enjoyment. If your
copy fails to meet our high standards,
please inform us and we will gladly
replace it.

www.musicsales.com

THE BIG BOOK OF COUNTRY

Hal Leonard Europe
Distributed by Music Sales

AIN'T GOIN' DOWN
('Til the Sun Comes Up)

Words and Music by KIM WILLIAMS,
GARTH BROOKS and KENT BLAZY

Six o'-clock on Fri - day eve-ning,
Nine o'-clock, the show is end-ing

Ma - ma does-n't know she's leav-ing 'til she hears the screen door slam-ming,
but the fun is just be - gin - ning. She knows he's an - tic - i - pat - ing,

back in bed be - fore the morn-ing."
danc - ing cheek to cheek.

They ain't go - ing down 'til the sun comes _ up, ain't _

_ giv - ing in 'til they get e-nough. Go - ing 'round the world in a

ANYMORE

Words and Music by TRAVIS TRITT
and JILL COLUCCI

BEFORE YOU KILL US ALL

Words and Music by KEITH FOLLESE
and MAX T. BARNES

20

BLUE

Words and Music by
BILL MACK

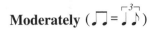

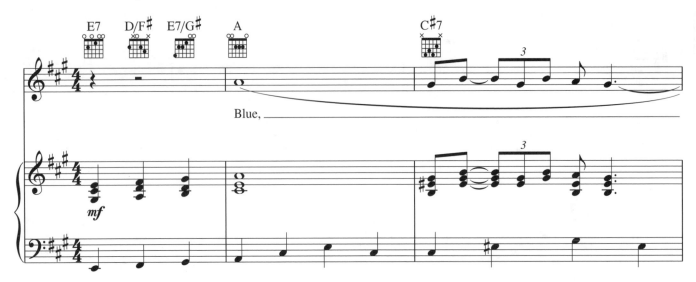

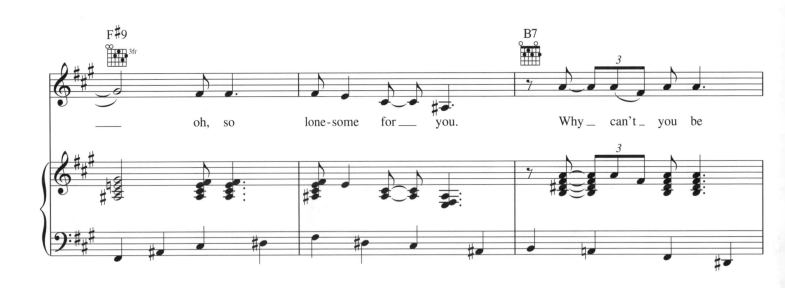

BLUE EYES CRYING IN THE RAIN

Words and Music by
FRED ROSE

CAN'T BE REALLY GONE

Words and Music by
GARY BURR

blocked the wind, __ it stopped __ the rain; she'd nev - er leave __ that one. __
like they're wait - ing in _____ the hall for her to slip __ them on. __

So, she can't be real - ly gone. _____

The

I don't know

when she'll come _ back. She must _ in - tend ___ to come _ back.

CODA

No, she can't be real - ly gone.

rit.

BLUE MOON OF KENTUCKY

Words and Music by
BILL MONROE

Bright jump tempo

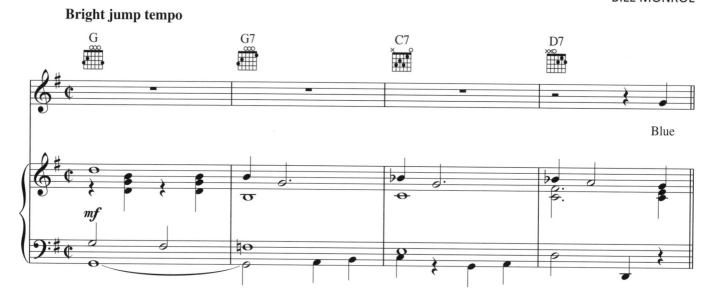

BOBBIE ANN MASON

Words and Music by
MARK D. SANDERS

BOOT SCOOTIN' BOOGIE

Words and Music by
RONNIE DUNN

CHECK YES OR NO

Words and Music by DANNY M. WELLS
and DANA H. OGLESBY

50

CRAZY

Words and Music by
WILLIE NELSON

D-I-V-O-R-C-E

Words and Music by BOBBY BRADDOCK
and CURLY PUTMAN

DOES THAT BLUE MOON EVER SHINE ON YOU

Words and Music by
TOBY KEITH

FRIENDS IN LOW PLACES

Words and Music by DEWAYNE BLACKWELL
and EARL BUD LEE

GONE COUNTRY

Words and Music by
BOB McDILL

She's been play-ing that ___ room ___ on the strip
folk scene's ___ dead, ___ but
mutes to L. A., ___ but

for ten years in the Ve - gas.
he's hold - ing out ___ in the vil - lage.
he's got a house ___ in the Val - ley.

Ev - 'ry night she looks ___ in the mir - ror, and she on - ly
He's been writ - ing songs, ___ speak - ing out a - gainst wealth and
But the bills are pil - ing up, and the pop scene just ain't gon - na

GREEN GREEN GRASS OF HOME

Words and Music by
CURLY PUTMAN

HEADS CAROLINA, TAILS CALIFORNIA

Words and Music by TIM NICHOLS
and MARK D. SANDERS

HYPNOTIZE THE MOON

Words and Music by STEVE DORFF
and ERIC KAZ

She knew she caught my eye ___
Once I held ___ her close; ___

and that was all ___ it took. ___ Ain't it
I knew just where ___ I stood. ___ No, you

strange how ___ for- ev - er changed ___ with just ___ one look?
nev - er get a sec- ond chance ___ to ev- er feel so good. ___

hyp - no - tize _____ moon. _____

HERE'S A QUARTER
(Call Someone Who Cares)

Words and Music by
TRAVIS TRITT

I CAN LOVE YOU LIKE THAT

Words and Music by STEVE DIAMOND,
MARIBETH DERRY and JENNIFER KIMBALL

I CAN'T STOP LOVING YOU

Words and Music by
DON GIBSON

I'M GONNA HIRE A WINO TO DECORATE OUR HOME

Words and Music by
DEWAYNE BLACKWELL

I'VE COME TO EXPECT IT FROM YOU

Words and Music by DEAN DILLON
and BUDDY CANNON

gone and done to me?_____ I would-n't
un - luck - y stars _____ that I'm a - live
next time do - in' me wrong. _____ You'll come

treat a dog____ the way _____ you treat - ed me.
and you're the way ____ you are.
back this time ____ to find____ out that I'm gone.__

But that's what I get. ___
But that's what I get. ___
But that's what I get. ___

I've come to ex - pect _____ it__ from you. _____
I've come to ex - pect _____ it__ from you. _____
you should ex - pect _____ that _ from me.

IF I WERE YOU

Words and Music by
TERRI CLARK

Slow Country ballad

standin' at __ my front door __ when
think you're miss - in' out on some - thin' be - cause you

IF THE GOOD DIE YOUNG

Words and Music by PAUL NELSON
and CRAIG WISEMAN

115

IF TOMORROW NEVER COMES

Words and Music by KENT BLAZY
and GARTH BROOKS

Some-times late at night, __
See additional lyrics

I lie a-wake and watch __ her sleep — ing. __

She's lost in peace-ful dreams, __ so I turn

Additional Lyrics

2. 'Cause I've lost loved ones in my life.
   Who never knew how much I loved them.
   Now I live with the regret
   That my true feelings for them never were revealed.
   So I made a promise to myself
   To say each day how much she means to me
   And avoid that circumstance
   Where there's no second chance to tell her how I feel. ('Cause)
   Chorus

IT MATTERS TO ME

Words and Music by ED HILL
and MARK D. SANDERS

IT'S MIDNIGHT CINDERELLA

Words and Music by KIM WILLIAMS,
KENT BLAZY and GARTH BROOKS

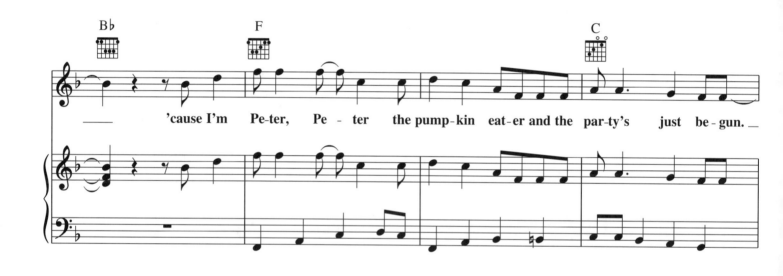

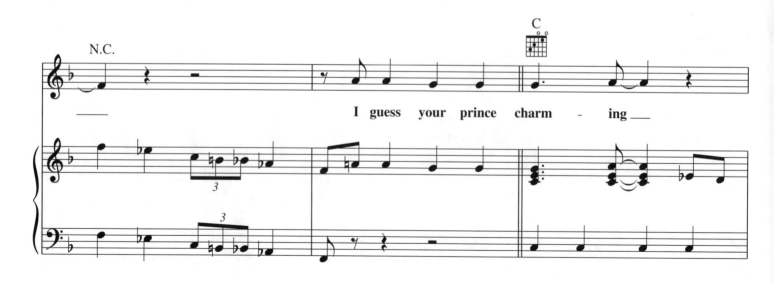

Pe - ter, Pe - ter the pump - kin eat - er and the par - ty's just be - gun.

THE KEEPER OF THE STARS

Words and Music by KAREN STALEY,
DANNY MAYO and DICKEY LEE

LIFE GOES ON

Words and Music by KEITH FOLLESE,
DEL GRAY and THOM McHUGH

LET'S GO TO VEGAS

Words and Music by
KAREN STALEY

kiss the sin - gle life good - bye. _____ Hey, ba - by, let's go to Ve - gas,

bet on love _ and let it ride.

LONELY TOO LONG

Words and Music by BILL RICE,
MARY SHARON RICE and MIKE LAWLER

153

MAMMAS DON'T LET YOUR BABIES GROW UP TO BE COWBOYS

Words and Music by ED BRUCE
and PATSY BRUCE

Country Waltz

Mam-mas don't let your ba-bies grow up ___ to be cow-boys.

Don't let 'em pick gui-tars and

drive them old trucks. Make 'em be doc-tors and law-yers and

MI VIDA LOCA
(My Crazy Life)

Words and Music by PAM TILLIS
and JESS LEARY

Sweet -

MY HEROES HAVE ALWAYS BEEN COWBOYS

Words and Music by
SHARON VAUGHN

MY MARIA

Words and Music by DANIEL J. MOORE
and B.W. STEVENSON

174

MY NEXT BROKEN HEART

Words and Music by DON COOK,
RONNIE DUNN and KIX BROOKS

NO ONE ELSE ON EARTH

Words and Music by SAM LORBER,
STEWART HARRIS and JILL COLUCCI

OKIE FROM MUSKOGEE

Words and Music by MERLE HAGGARD
and ROY EDWARD BURRIS

Moderately fast

mf

Eb

1. We don't smoke mar - i - jua - na in Mus - ko - gee,
2. We don't make a par - ty out of lov - ing,
   boots are still in style if a man needs foot - wear,

And we don't take our trips on L. S.
But we like hold - ing hands and pitch - ing
Beads and Ro - man san - dals won't be

ON THE OTHER HAND

Words and Music by DON SCHLITZ
and PAUL OVERSTREET

ONE MORE LAST CHANCE

Words and Music by GARY NICHOLSON
and VINCE GILL

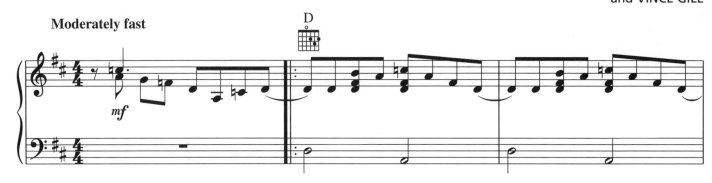

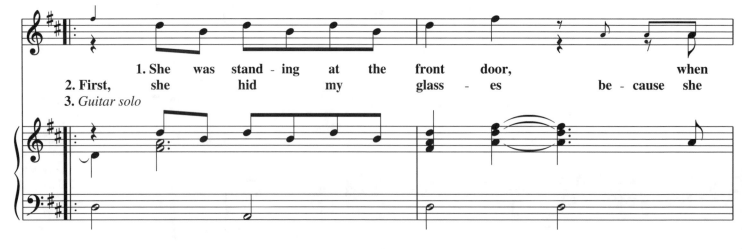

1. She was stand - ing at the front door, when
2. First, she hid my glass - es be - cause she
3. *Guitar solo*

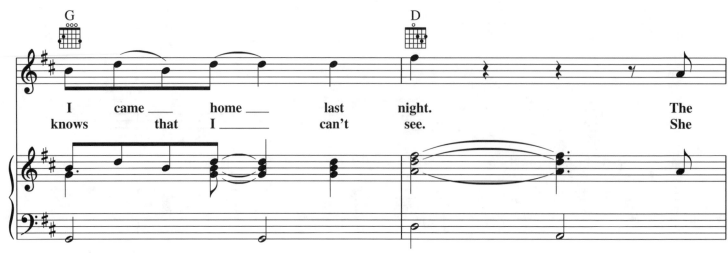

I came ___ home ___ last night. The
knows that I ___ can't see. She

RUMOR HAS IT

Words and Music by LARRY SHELL,
VERN DANT and BRUCE BURCH

Moderate country ballad

I over heard a conver-
town's so small, a

-sation your name was mentioned
whisper can be heard a mile a-

in but they didn't talk a-
-way, and people here will

198

PLEASE REMEMBER ME

Words and Music by RODNEY CROWELL
and WILL JENNINGS

Original key: Db major. This edition has been transposed down one half-step to be more playable.

mem - ber me. ___

SHE'S EVERY WOMAN

Words and Music by VICTORIA SHAW
and GARTH BROOKS

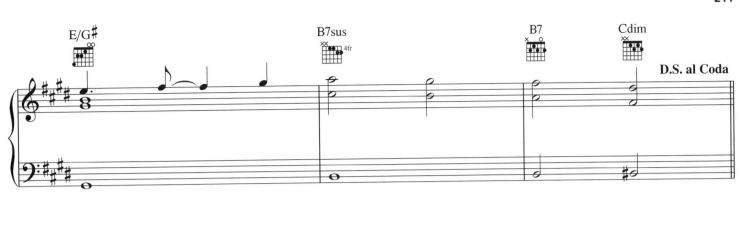

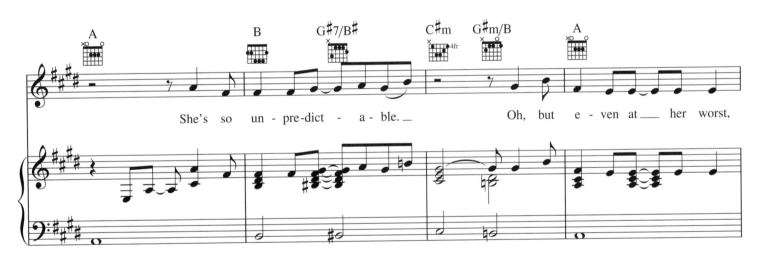

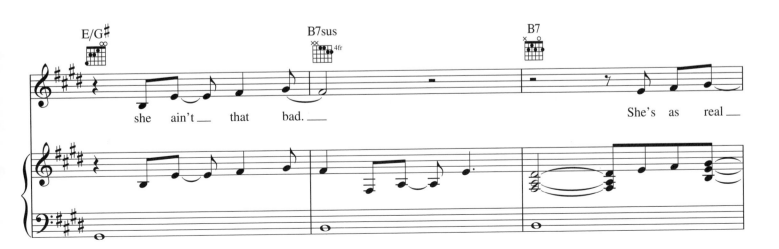

SLEEPING SINGLE IN A DOUBLE BED

Words and Music by DENNIS MORGAN
and KYE FLEMING

sin-gle in a dou-ble bed. *Instrumental*

SHE'S NOT THE CHEATIN' KIND

Words and Music by
RONNIE DUNN

Oh, ___ she's _____ not the cheat - in' kind. _

_____ She's been cheat - ed one _

SOMEWHERE IN THE VICINITY OF THE HEART

Words and Music by BILL LABOUNTY
and RICK CHUDACOFF

TALL, TALL TREES

Words and Music by GEORGE JONES
and ROGER MILLER

SWEET DREAMS

Words and Music by
DON GIBSON

TEN THOUSAND ANGELS

Words and Music by STEVEN DALE JONES
and BILLY HENDERSON

TENNESSEE WALTZ

Words and Music by REDD STEWART
and PEE WEE KING

Lyrics: much I have lost. Yes I lost my lit-tle dar-lin' the night they were play-ing the beau-ti-ful Ten-nes-see Waltz. I was Waltz.

TILL YOU LOVE ME

Words and Music by GARY BURR
and BOB DiPIERO

TO BE LOVED BY YOU

Words and Music by GARY BURR
and MIKE REID

UNTANGLIN' MY MIND

Words and Music by MERLE HAGGARD
and CLINT BLACK

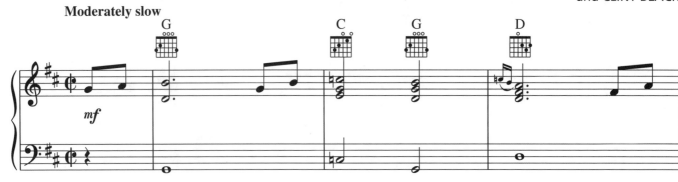

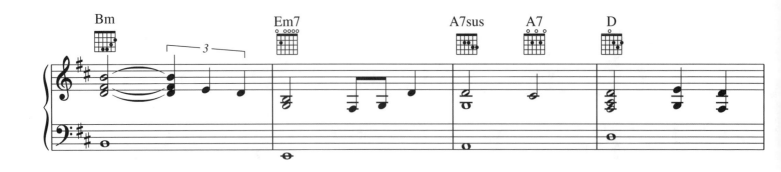

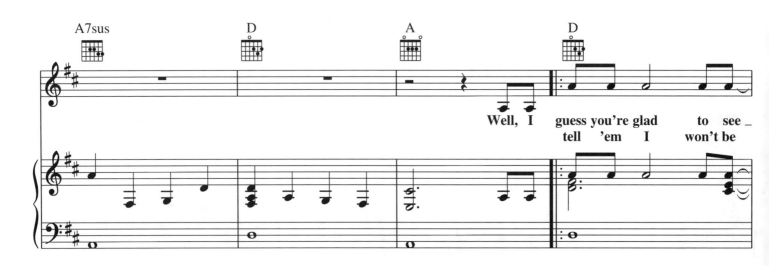

Well, I guess you're glad to see _
tell 'em I won't be

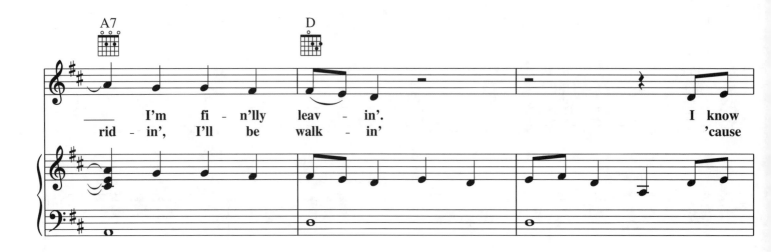

I'm fi - n'lly leav - in'.
rid - in', I'll be walk - in'

I know
'cause

WHEN A WOMAN LOVES A MAN

Words and Music by RAFE VanHOY
and MARK LUNA

WHAT MATTERED MOST

Words and Music by GARY BURR
and VINCE MELAMED

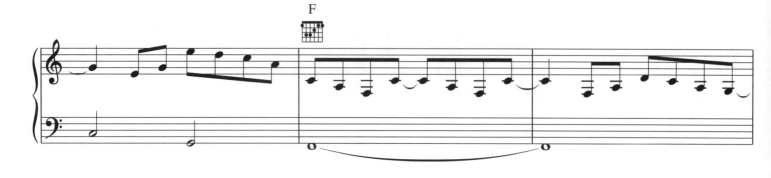

I thought _ I knew _

the girl _ so _ well.
she nev - er _____ said.

Repeat and Fade

WHEN YOU SAY NOTHING AT ALL

Words and Music by PAUL OVERSTREET
and DON SCHLITZ

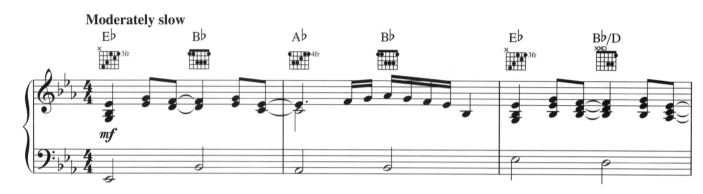

It's a-maz - ing how _ you can speak right _ to my heart. _

All day long _ I can hear peo - ple talk - ing out loud, _

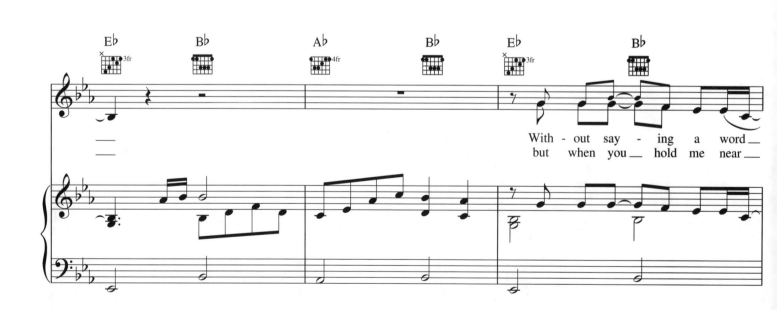

With - out say - ing a word

but when you _ hold me near _

truth in your eyes ____ say - ing you'll ____ nev - er leave ____ me.   A

touch of your hand ____ says you'll catch ____ me if ev - er I fall. ____

Now you say it best ____   when you say noth - ing at all. __

To Coda ⊕

WHICH BRIDGE TO CROSS
(Which Bridge to Burn)

Words and Music by BILL ANDERSON
and VINCE GILL

WILD ANGELS

Words and Music by HARRY STINSON,
MATRACA BERG and GARY HARRISON

WILD ONE

Words and Music by WILL RAMBEAUX,
JAIME KYLE and PAT BUNCH

WORKIN' MAN BLUES

Words and Music by
MERLE HAGGARD

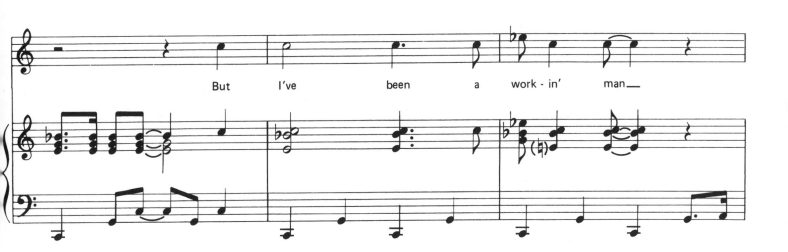

2. I keep my nose on the grindstone, work hard everyday.
   I might get a little tired on the weekend, after I draw my pay.
   I'll go back workin', come Monday morning I'm right back with the crew.
   And I drink a little beer that evening,
     Sing a little bit of these workin' man blues.

3. Sometimes I think about leaving, do a little bumming around.
   I want to throw my bills out the window, catch a train to another town.
   I'll go back workin', gotta buy my kids a brand new pair of shoes.
   I drink a little beer in a tavern,
     Cry a little bit of these workin' man blues.

4. Well, Hey! Hey! The workin' man, the workin' man like me
   I ain't never been on welfare, that's one place I won't be.
   I'll be workin', long as my two hands are fit to use.
   I'll drink my beer in a tavern,
     Sing a little bit of these workin' man blues.

XXX's and OOO's
(An American Girl)

Words and Music by ALICE RANDALL
and MATRACA BERG

YOU CAN FEEL BAD

Words and Music by TIM KREKEL
and MATRACA BERG

The car's   run-ning and your
May-be   I'll go_____

YOU CAN'T MAKE A HEART LOVE SOMEBODY

Words and Music by STEVE CLARK
and JOHNNY MacRAE

YOU'RE STILL THE ONE

Words and Music by SHANIA TWAIN
and R.J. LANGE